A Cook's
Record
Book

A Cook's Record Book

Bridget Jones

LORENZ BOOKS

This edition published in 1997 by Lorenz Books

Lorenz Books is an imprint of
Anness Publishing Limited
Hermes House
88-89 Blackfriars Road
London SE1 8HA

© 1997 Anness Publishing Limited

ISBN 1 86957 492 5

A CIP catalogue record for this book is available from the British Library

Publisher: Joanna Lorenz
Editorial Manager: Helen Sudell
Copy Editor: Jenni Fleetwood
Designer: Bet Ayer
Photographs: Michelle Garrett, Don Last, Amanda Heywood
Home Economists: Joanna Farrow, Bridget Jones, Christine France, Norma MacMillan, Carole Clements

*For all recipes, quantities are given in both metric and imperial measures
and, where appropriate, measures are also given in standard cups and spoons.
Follow one set, but not a mixture, because they are not interchangeable.*

Printed and bound in China

3 5 7 9 10 8 6 4 2

Contents

INTRODUCTION

Food is such a fabulously varied subject that there is always something new to discover. Exciting ingredients appear on supermarket shelves throughout the seasons and there are always new delicatessen products and health-food ingredients to sample. Making notes is an excellent way of preserving your experience for future reference.

This record book will take the place of all those scrappy bits of paper, packet tops, menu cards, jottings on paper napkins and notes on the calendar about your friends' latest eating habits. With this diary of culinary happenings, never again will you panic five minutes before guests arrive for dinner because you have a vague recollection that one of them may be allergic to an ingredient in the main dish.

In the pages that follow you will find guidance on all aspects of food, from topical subjects, like eating healthily, to traditions and taboos. There are reminders of seasonal specialities, menu planning, family celebrations, checklists and guest lists for all occasions. Space is provided for making notes and lists on all sorts of food-related subjects.

The book also lets you record what you served to whom and when. Next time you go for a repeat culinary performance, your personal recipe notes and guest list will ensure you are not only confident it will be just as successful as last time, but also that this time round the same stunning recipes will delight a different audience.

Nature's bounty: a gift to the cook.

EAT WELL, STAY WELL

Keeping a record of the fruit and vegetables you eat is a good starting point for checking your diet. Fried potatoes, roast potatoes, fruit fritters and other high-fat items do not count; include only boiled, steamed, stir-fried and raw ingredients. If week one falls far short of the recommended five portions a day, try to reform your eating habits, then record the higher number of portions eaten in week two.

This is also a good system for checking (and adjusting) the balance of other foods in your diet – high-fibre and starchy foods, for example. Adapt the record system to monitor the number of fibre-rich portions of food you eat or the starchy foods, like potatoes or rice.

The system can also be useful for admitting to over-indulgence, by recording high-fat, over-sweet or rich foods. A record that reveals a daily indulgence in cream cakes, fried potatoes and luscious desserts is a sure sign that your diet needs re-balancing!

Remember, though, that eating is meant to be a pleasure. Making the occasional dietary check is an excellent way of attempting to maintain a good balance but do not allow your life to be ruled by what you can or cannot eat.

EXAMPLES OF FRUIT AND VEGETABLES TO INCLUDE IN YOUR DAILY RECORD
* Apples, pears, oranges, bananas, grapes, plums, peaches, soft fruit, canned fruit in juice, frozen fruit in desserts.
* Cabbage, spinach, leeks, Brussels sprouts, spring greens, peas and beans.
* Carrots, parsnips, swedes, celeriac and turnips.
* Celery and fennel.

* Salad ingredients: many of those already listed, served raw; also lettuce, tomatoes, cucumber, watercress and Chinese cabbage; lightly boiled frozen vegetables, such as peas, broad beans, French beans, sweetcorn or mixed vegetables.

Breads and other baked goods should make up the bulk of your diet, but go easy on the butter and jam.

STARCHY FOODS TO MAKE UP THE BULK OF YOUR DIET
* Bread: all types of wholemeal and white.
* Potatoes: baked or boiled; mashed with a little butter, milk and plenty of seasoning.
* Rice: white, brown, basmati, wild.
* Pearl barley, couscous, cracked wheat.
* Lentils (red, green, brown or black), kidney beans, chick-peas, flageolet beans, haricot beans, borlotti beans, butter beans.
* Pasta: all types of fresh or dried.

TWO-WEEK FRUIT AND VEGETABLE RECORD

	WEEK 1 Fruit and Vegetable Portions	WEEK 2 Fruit and Vegetable Portions
Monday		
Tuesday		
Wednesday		
Thursday		
Friday		
Saturday		
Sunday		

✳ VEGETABLE TIP: A basic mixture of cooked vegetables in a cheese sauce (cauliflower florets, diced carrots, chunks of new potatoes, sliced mushrooms, celery and so on) is extremely versatile. Serve it in baked potatoes, with rice or couscous, in wheat tortillas or with a crunchy baked breadcrumb and cheese topping.

DRESSINGS AND TOPPINGS

Using modest amounts of fat is not too difficult in many dishes and cooking methods – grilling, stir-frying, boiling, steaming, poaching, stewing and braising can all be adapted to use little added fat – but serve a salad completely naked of dressing or a dessert that begs for cream without a little topping and there is an immediate sense of loss. Low-fat fromage frais and yogurt are the standard alternatives, but they can be a little tasteless.

Flavoured vinegars are good for simple dressings.

SALAD DRESSINGS

Drenching a refreshing salad with an oily dressing or generous dollops of creamy mayonnaise changes a light starter or side dish into a high-fat course. Try these alternatives.

* Light soy sauce, fresh lemon juice and a few drops of sesame oil make a delicious dressing for sliced mushrooms sprinkled with chopped spring onions.
* Whisk the juice of 1 orange with seasoning and 10ml/2 tsp olive oil, stir in some chopped fresh parsley and snipped chives, then use to dress green salad, fennel salad or coarsely grated carrots.
* Buy fairly firm low-fat soft cheese, avoiding the type which contains starch as a thickener, and stir in just enough milk, low-fat fromage frais or plain yogurt to give a soft creamy consistency. Add salt and pepper and chopped herbs (chives make a nice addition), then use to dress coleslaw-type salads.

VEGETABLE TOPPINGS

Try these instead of adding large amounts of butter to vegetables.

* Sprinkle roasted sesame seeds over boiled potatoes, spinach, carrots or cabbage.
* Mix 5ml/1 tsp wholegrain mustard and a handful of chopped fresh mint with 15ml/1 tbsp olive oil. Use to dress new potatoes, cabbage, carrots, Brussels sprouts or peas.
* Mix chopped fresh parsley and snipped chives into low-fat soft cheese and serve with baked potatoes.
* Mix 30ml/2 tbsp finely grated fresh Parmesan cheese with 30ml/2 tbsp each of chopped fresh parsley and toasted breadcrumbs. Sprinkle over steamed or boiled vegetables.

DESSERT APPEAL

A coating of cream or swirl of rich Greek-style yogurt works wonders on almost any dessert, but there are lower fat alternatives.

* Sweeten low-fat fromage frais lightly with icing sugar and stir in a little natural vanilla essence.
* Gradually thin low-fat soft cheese to a pouring consistency with a little apple juice and serve instead of cream.
* Lightly sweeten low-fat soft cheese with honey or maple syrup and use to fill gâteaux or serve as a dessert topping.

Low-fat choices can taste as good as cream.

DIETARY RESTRICTIONS

Enter the foods that friends MUST avoid on the dietary record page opposite, rather than likes and dislikes, which are not potentially dangerous. When cooking for anyone with a professionally diagnosed food intolerance, remember not to include that food anywhere in the dishes served for the meal. In some cases, an allergic response can be sparked by even minimum contamination from the ingredient, such as cross-contamination from serving spoons.

Diabetes

Avoid significant amounts of all types of sugars, including honey, syrups and treacle. Since this condition is more common than some others, a separate page of notes and recipe ideas is included.

Fats

Some conditions are aggravated by high-fat meals. As well as restrictions on the level of fat, the type of fat eaten may be important; for example, saturated fats may be avoided, so animal fats should be replaced by less-saturated vegetable fats.

Gluten Intolerance

Sufferers from colic disease cannot digest gluten, a protein substance found in wheat. All wheat products must be avoided, including all types of wheat flour and products containing them. Avoid pasta, bread, bulgur, cracked wheat and any products containing wheat starch or flour. Remember that thickeners may be used in products like yogurt, so it is best to avoid convenience items unless you are certain that they do not contain gluten. Gluten-free products, including alternatives to flour, are available from healthfood shops.

For those who cannot have milk, there are plenty of tasty and nutritious alternatives.

Milk

Some people cannot tolerate the carbohydrate (lactose) in milk. All milk products – such as butter, cheese, cream and yogurt – should be avoided. Soya milk is a useful substitute.

Nuts

These can produce a mild asthmatic reaction and in some cases a rapid and severe response. Peanuts can be particularly dangerous and have occasionally proved lethal. Avoid all products containing nuts and nut oils, such as groundnut oil. Do not even sprinkle a topping of nuts on a dish or mix nuts with other snacks served with drinks. Carefully read the labels on any convenience items you purchase.

Shellfish

Prawns, mussels, oysters, scallops and other shellfish can produce a rapid reaction in those who are allergic to them. Some people are simply paranoid about possible effects. If there is any doubt, change the menu.

DIETARY RESTRICTIONS RECORD

NAME	FOODS TO AVOID	DATE

✳ TIP: If at all possible, when entertaining friends with special food requirements, make a meal which will suit them and everybody else, even if it means offering a choice of desserts or starters. Menus adapted to fit certain dietary restrictions need not be tasteless. Being singled out as the person who cannot eat a certain dish is very depressing, and quite embarrassing.

DIABETIC MEALS

Anyone with diabetes will follow a diet based on the general guidelines for balanced eating, with additional restrictions on the consumption of all types of sugar and products using sugar.

When entertaining someone with diabetes, the main thing to remember is to avoid using significant quantities of sugar in any form. This includes honey, syrups and treacle as well as all dry forms of sugar.

Avoiding sugar in one meal is not a problem as fruit can be made into interesting sugar-free desserts and artificial sweeteners can be used. If you have a diabetic guest for a weekend, the following tips may prove helpful.

✳ Follow the rules for a balanced diet, avoiding too much fat and including plenty of fresh fruit, vegetables and starchy foods.
✳ Offer wholemeal bread and crackers, and high-fibre breakfast cereals.

Wholemeal bread is a good choice for diabetics.

✳ Buy unsweetened breakfast cereals – check the information on the packet and you may be surprised at the sugar content of many cereals.
✳ Offer skimmed or semi-skimmed milk for breakfast.
✳ An unsweetened fresh fruit salad, sprinkled with toasted rolled oats and finely chopped hazelnuts served with natural low-fat yogurt makes a tempting breakfast. Include sweet fruit, such as mango, pear and banana with fresh orange or another equally refreshing ingredient.

A tempting fruit platter.

✳ Avoid sweet preserves and jams. Look out for sugar-free preserves recommended for use in a diabetic diet.
✳ Use artificial sweeteners to sweeten fruit purées, cold soufflés, mousses and other cold desserts. Some types of artificial sweetener lose their sweet taste when cooked, so add them to hot sauces, stewed fruits and similar dishes after cooking.
✳ Remember that many commercial savoury sauces may contain a significant amount of sugar. Chutneys and some pickles usually have a high sugar content.
✳ Sweetened cakes, biscuits and confectionery should be avoided. Unsweetened currant buns, wholemeal fruit loaves and sugar-free biscuits or plain wholemeal biscuits are usually acceptable. Diabetic chocolates and confectionery are available from chemists and some healthfood shops sell sugar-free items.

RELIGIOUS RESTRICTIONS

In their teachings, many religions include periods of fasting or rules on foods which should not be eaten. It is a good idea to check if you are formally entertaining guests from another culture or religious background; for example, at a wedding or if you are arranging a business function. Close friends and acquaintances will invariably let you know of any foods they avoid.

Buddhism
Buddhists are usually vegetarian as their religion forbids the killing of animals for food.

Some people still prefer to eat only fish on Fridays.

Walnut pilaff is an ideal vegetarian dish.

Islam
Muslims fast between sunrise and sunset during Ramadan – the ninth month of the Muslim year.

Christianity
Christians often observe periods of fasting. For example, many people prefer to avoid certain foods during Lent, the period of 40 days from Ash Wednesday until Easter Sunday.

Hinduism
Hindus avoid beef as the cow is regarded as sacred. There are many sects within the religion and various food laws. Some Hindus are vegetarian or vegan and alcohol is forbidden.

Judaism
Jews observe complicated kosher food laws on the slaughtering of animals and preparation of foods when following their religion strictly, but they would be unlikely to expect non-Jews to master such details. Most Jews avoid pork (and all pig products) and shell-fish (fish is acceptable). They may also avoid eating dairy foods with meat.

USEFUL RECIPES

If you do not make a record of a wonderfully successful dish you adapted for a particular meal, you will never remember the details when you want to repeat the performance. Friends who avoid certain foods for health, religious or cultural reasons are often happy to share their favourite recipes. Remember to make a note of the ingredient each recipe excludes, if applicable.

RECIPE TITLE	RECIPE TITLE
INGREDIENT EXCLUDED	INGREDIENT EXCLUDED
DATE	DATE
INGREDIENTS	INGREDIENTS
METHOD	METHOD
NOTES	NOTES

✱ TIP: When substituting an unusual ingredient in a special recipe (gluten-free pasta is a good example) make a note of the shop where you purchased the product and the name and address of the manufacturer, then you can always contact one or the other for information or if you cannot find a similar product in future.

RECIPE TITLE

INGREDIENT EXCLUDED

DATE

INGREDIENTS

METHOD

NOTES

RECIPE TITLE

INGREDIENT EXCLUDED

DATE

INGREDIENTS

METHOD

NOTES

Vegetarian Menus

True vegetarians do not eat any meat whatsoever. But there are varying degrees and some people avoid red meat, eating only poultry and fish, or include only fish in their diets. There are two types of vegetarian diet.

Lacto-vegetarian Diet
This excludes all fish, poultry, meat and game but it includes animal products obtained without the animal being killed; milk and its products and eggs are eaten.

Vegan Diet
This excludes all animal products, including dairy foods. Vegans rely solely on vegetable foods for protein; without particular attention a vegan diet can be deficient in nutrients found in animal foods, such as vitamin B12.

A vegan meal contains no animal products.

Vegetarian Ingredients
These ingredients are eaten by some vegetarians but those who are strict will avoid them.

Cheese
Some lacto-vegetarians avoid ordinary cheese as rennet, a product from the stomach of calves, is used to curdle the milk. Vegetarian cheese is available, made with an alternative culture to rennet.

Eggs
Many vegetarians do not like plain cooked eggs but may eat them when incorporated in dishes.

Gelatine
Agar-agar can be used instead of gelatine – it is a tasteless seaweed product. Agar gives a firmer, less elastic texture than gelatine.

Mincemeat
Mincemeat usually contains beef suet; look for vegetarian mincemeat or make your own with vegetable suet.

Quorn
This is a savoury myco-protein product, grown in the same way as mushrooms; however, the egg whites used to grow Quorn are not taken from free-range eggs, so some vegetarians avoid it.

Suet
Ordinary suet is the thick layer of fat surrounding internal organs. It is shredded and coated in flour. Most vegetarians substitute vegetable suet.

Protein Reminders
If one of your family changes to a vegetarian diet or vegetarian guests stay for a few days, it is sensible to know which foods provide the proteins usually derived from fish and meat. Dairy foods (eggs, cheese, milk) are good sources, but eating too high a proportion does not give a well-balanced diet. Soy beans and soya products, such as beancurd, provide the most complete source of vegetable protein. Nuts are also rich in protein. Other pulses contain protein, including lentils, kidney beans and other beans. Beansprouts are also a good source. To achieve the right balance, beans and pulses, grains and cereals and a good supply of vegetables should be included regularly.

VEGETARIAN FRIENDS RECORD

NAME	TYPE OF VEGETARIAN DIET

 # VEGETARIAN MENUS RECORD

DATE	DATE
OCCASION	OCCASION
GUESTS	GUESTS
MENU	MENU
DATE	DATE
OCCASION	OCCASION
GUESTS	GUESTS
MENU	MENU

✱ MACROBIOTIC TIP: A macrobiotic diet consists of vegetables grown and prepared without chemicals. Anyone seriously following a macrobiotic diet will usually be vegan and will consume only organic ingredients. The principles of yin and yang energies, or forces, influence the choice and mix of foods eaten. It is a good idea to make up a main course of several different kinds of simple vegetable dishes, allowing the guest flexibility in the mixture of food eaten.

BULGUR WHEAT SALAD WITH HERBS

Bulgur wheat, a nutritious grain, is made by steaming whole wheat berries and then drying and cracking them.

Serves 6

INGREDIENTS
115g/4oz/1 cup bulgur
wheat
225g/8oz tomatoes,
seeded and diced
1 small red onion
3 spring onions, chopped
55g/2oz parsley, finely
chopped
60ml/4 tbsps fresh mint, chopped
120ml/4fl oz/1/2 cup olive oil or vegetable oil
75ml/5 tbsps lemon juice
salt and pepper
black olives and mint leaves, to garnish

Put the bulgur in a sieve and rinse under cold running water until the water runs clear. Place the bulgur in a bowl, cover with fresh cold water and soak for 1 hour or until plump. Drain, pressing out all excess moisture.

Combine the bulgur with all the ingredients in a large bowl. Stir to mix the ingredients thoroughly. Taste and adjust the seasoning if necessary. Serve the salad at room temperature, garnished with black olives and mint leaves, if desired.

SPICY VEGETABLE STEW WITH COUSCOUS

Couscous makes a good basis for a stew and is an excellent filler for all your vegan friends.

Serves 4

INGREDIENTS
25ml/1 1/2 tbsp vegetable
oil
2 large onions, cut into
chunks
2.5ml/1/2 tsp ground
cumin
1.5ml/1/2 tsp ground
cinnamon
1/4 tsp turmeric
350g/12oz carrots, cut into chunks
350g/12oz courgettes, cut into chunks
350g/12oz turnip, cut into chunks
1 1/2 pints/900ml/3 3/4 cups chicken or vegetable stock
1 red pepper, seeded and cut into large squares
40g/1 1/2oz/1/3 cup raisins
350g/12oz/2 cups quick-cooking couscous
25g/1oz butter
150g/5oz/1 cup thawed frozen peas
salt and pepper

Heat the oil in a pot. Cook the onions and spices for 1 minute. Add the carrots, turnips and 150ml/1/4 pint/1/3 cup of the stock. Bring to the boil and cook for 5 minutes. Add the courgettes, red pepper and raisins. Simmer for 10 minutes. Prepare the couscous, using the remaining stock and the butter. Add the peas to the stew and cook for 3–5 minutes, then season. Divide the couscous among hot bowls. Make a well in the centre of each and spoon in the vegetable stew.

FAVOURITE VEGETARIAN RECIPES

RECIPE TITLE	RECIPE TITLE
FROM	FROM
DATE	DATE
SERVES	SERVES
INGREDIENTS	INGREDIENTS
METHOD	METHOD
NOTES	NOTES

✱ VEGETARIAN TIP: Canned flageolet beans (drained) and sliced mushrooms make a delicious filling for lasagne: layer them with the lasagne, adding crumbled dolcelatte cheese and coat with a béchamel sauce. Sprinkle a little grated Parmesan cheese over the top layer of sauce before baking.

RECIPE TITLE	RECIPE TITLE
FROM	FROM
DATE	DATE
SERVES	SERVES
INGREDIENTS	INGREDIENTS
METHOD	METHOD
NOTES	NOTES

✽ VEGETARIAN TIP: Cashew nuts and apple juice make a tasty dessert topping instead of dairy cream. Grind 175g/6oz/1 cup unsalted cashew nuts in a blender, then gradually pour in 250ml/8fl oz/1 cup unsweetened apple juice with the motor running to make a thick cream. Chill before serving.

LIKES AND DISLIKES

It is safe to assume that most people enjoy all the usual foods and the onus is on guests with particular food hates to let you know in advance. However, when you are cooking for acquaintances and guests you do not know very well, it is a good idea to avoid certain ingredients.

Baked Eggs

Everyone has their own idea about the perfectly cooked egg and soft baked eggs with a slightly runny white are not to everyone's taste. Poached eggs can also be difficult: some people like them very runny while others loathe whites that are not firmly set.

Before serving game, make sure your guests like it.

Game

Pheasant is usually a safe choice (unless it is really well hung and very gamey) but some people do not like the pronounced flavour of game birds and venison.

Offal

Apart from meat sauces and stuffings enriched with chicken livers, it is unwise to serve offal unless you are sure guests will enjoy it. It is also a good idea to serve a simple alternative to pâtés; for example, an interesting salad which could either complement the pâté or be an alternative first course.

Rare Meat

Unless you know friends appreciate rare meat, it is best to ensure that joints are medium or well cooked.

Most people like prawns and shrimps but it never hurts to check with your guests.

Seafood and Shellfish in the Shell

Prawns and shrimps are rarely unacceptable, but mussels, cockles, clams, whelks and oysters are not universally appreciated. Squid and octopus are not always welcome.

Veal

This is sometimes avoided by those who eat all other forms of meat.

LIKES AND DISLIKES RECORD

NAME	NAME
DATE	DATE
LIKES	LIKES
DISLIKES	DISLIKES

NAME	NAME
DATE	DATE
LIKES	LIKES
DISLIKES	DISLIKES

✴ ENTERTAINING TIP: Keep a good-quality bought or home-made citrus fruit sorbet in the freezer as a standby should anyone not want the planned starter or dessert. The sorbet will go with melon, avocado, papaya or a salad of cherry tomatoes or cucumber to make a first course. For dessert it may be served with most fruit (including soft fruit), biscuits, yogurt or cream.

DINNER PARTY REMINDERS

Ensuring that a formal dinner party is a memorable success takes planning, especially when you intend filling the dining room to capacity and inviting acquaintances you do not know extremely well.

✳ Invite guests who are likely to get on well. If you include somebody not intimate with your other guests, try to introduce some common ground and make every effort to integrate them.

✳ Make sure you have enough table space and chairs to seat everyone comfortably.

✳ Ring around to check that everyone is free, with two possible dates if necessary, then confirm the arrangements. For a formal meal, make arrangements about four weeks ahead and send out written invitations or confirmation. When inviting close friends, you know how far in advance their diaries are likely to fill up, but remember that summer holidays, Christmas and other national holidays tend to be quite busy.

✳ Plan the menu at least a week ahead (longer for a formal meal or if you have to order specialist ingredients), check the storecupboard and make a shopping list. Buy fresh foods as near as possible to the day.

✳ Make a list of things to do and when to do them: dishes to make in advance (perhaps they can be frozen or have to be chilled), ingredients to prepare early on the day and items that have to be completed at the last minute (keep these to a minimum).

✳ Check table linen beforehand and launder it if necessary. Make sure the house is tidy.

✳ Put white wine in the fridge to chill well in advance. Ensure you have plenty of soft drinks for any drivers or non-drinkers.

✳ Enhance the atmosphere by placing vases of flowers in prominent positions. Put candles in the centre of the table and scent the air by burning a little essential oil.

✳ Allow enough time for yourself after all the preparation so that you can bathe and dress calmly, then relax with your guests.

LEFT: *Small decorative touches can really make a difference when it comes to setting the scene.*

RIGHT: *Suit the table setting to the mood and style of the occasion.*

DINNER PARTY RECORD

Making a note of dinner parties, the menus and guests invited, provides an excellent source of inspiration and information for future occasions. Favourite dishes or menu combinations can be repeated without serving them to the same friends on several occasions, and disasters can be avoided a second time.

DATE	DATE
OCCASION	OCCASION
GUESTS	GUESTS
MENU	MENU
NOTES	NOTES

✱ DINNER PARTY TIP: Stretch streaky bacon rashers out thinly with the back of a knife, then wind them around breadsticks (grissini) and place on a lightly greased baking sheet. Grill or bake until crisp and browned. Serve as an accompaniment for soups or salad starters.

DATE

OCCASION

GUESTS

MENU

NOTES

DATE

OCCASION

GUESTS

MENU

NOTES

DATE

OCCASION

GUESTS

MENU

NOTES

DATE

OCCASION

GUESTS

MENU

NOTES

✱ DINNER PARTY TIP: Instead of buying chocolates to serve with coffee, dip walnut halves and brazil nuts in melted chocolate and set them to dry on waxed paper. Arrange in a dish with a selection of dried apricots, figs and dates, crystallized ginger and candied pineapple.

BIRTHDAY TREATS

Children usually have definite ideas of their own and they soon let you know what they consider to be the perfect birthday treat. However, on adult occasions, it is easy to slip into a celebration routine with the obligatory cake in a similar style every year. Planning something a little different may take some extra time and imagination but can be great fun. Whoevers birthday it is, be really creative and think about what that person particularly enjoys and would consider a speical treat. Remember to start planning well in advance if you want to invite lots of people, or book up some sort of popular activity. Be very careful about organizing a surprise party – it is amazing just how many people do not like them.

Decorative details help to make a birthday treat really special.

Candles create instant atmosphere.

CELEBRATION IDEAS

✳ Plan a picnic outing for a summer birthday. Visit a country park, organise family games or plan a walk. A sophisticated picnic for two, four or more can be taken to an outdoor concert, with a splendid menu, sparkling wine and everyone dressed up for the occasion.

✳ Organize a treasure hunt for a small group of friends. Plan well ahead, mapping out the entire route and making up the clues, then round off the event with a party. Simple treasure hunts can be based on a local walk, discovering places of interest that are often totally ignored on a daily basis. The final stage could lead to a wine merchant's with a special prize bottle awaiting the winner!

RIGHT: *Sundaes are popular every day of the week.*

✳ Think up a theme for a dinner party. For example, have a fondue, a Japanese menu, a seafood lunch menu or an exercise party followed by brunch.

NOT A BIRTHDAY CAKE!

Here are a some treats to make instead of a cake.

Sherry trifle – always a treat.

Celebration Trifle

Make a trifle, with a plain sponge cake as a base, jam, a few fresh raspberries, custard and whipped cream. Moisten the cake well with sherry or a liqueur. Decorate the top with fruit, whipped cream, ratafia biscuits, flaked almonds, grated chocolate, crystallized ginger or any other suitable ingredients.

Fun-day Sundaes

Make spectacular sundaes and decorate them with indoor sparklers and cocktail novelties. Select tall

glasses and fill them with layers of fresh fruit, fruit syrup, good vanilla ice cream, chopped nuts, and coarsely grated chocolate. Top with scoops of ice cream and decorate with exotic fruit. Add whipped cream and sparklers. Light the sparklers and carry the sundaes into a darkened room for full effect.

BIRTHDAY CHECKLIST

Keep a record of birthdays and other celebrations. Looking back at party ideas, menus and guest lists is great fun and it always provides inspiration for the next annual event!

NAME	NAME
BIRTHDAY	BIRTHDAY
YEAR	YEAR
CELEBRATION THEME	CELEBRATION THEME
MENU	MENU
GUESTS	GUESTS

✳ BIRTHDAY TIP: Make a note of friends' ages if they are likely to be celebrating a "memorable" birthday in the next couple of years. It is far easier to note down a passing comment than to spend weeks – or months – desperately trying to extract the date without asking a direct question.

NAME _____

BIRTHDAY _____

YEAR _____

CELEBRATION THEME _____

MENU _____

_____

_____

GUESTS _____

_____

_____

_____

NAME _____

BIRTHDAY _____

YEAR _____

CELEBRATION THEME _____

MENU _____

_____

_____

GUESTS _____

_____

_____

_____

NAME _____

BIRTHDAY _____

YEAR _____

CELEBRATION THEME _____

MENU _____

_____

_____

GUESTS _____

_____

_____

_____

NAME _____

BIRTHDAY _____

YEAR _____

CELEBRATION THEME _____

MENU _____

_____

_____

GUESTS _____

_____

_____

_____

A DRINKS PARTY

Mulled cider with sliced fruit.

Entertaining friends, formally or without pomp and ceremony, does not always have to involve cooking a meal. Drinks parties can be sociable and relaxing occasions.

WINES AND DRINKS

* Decide on the type or selection of drinks and limit the choice to these; do not offer a random selection or throw open the drinks cupboard.

* Red and white wine are acceptable as the only choice, with alcohol-free alternatives, of course.

* Good-quality sparkling wine or champagne is always acceptable, and there is no need to offer red wine as an alternative.

* Mulled wine or cider is ideal for winter parties and a light fruit punch based on white wine or red wine (sangria) works well in summer.

* Dry cider makes a superb base for fruit punch.

ALCOHOL-FREE ALTERNATIVES

* Buy plenty of sparkling and still mineral water. Offer ice, lemon, lime, orange or a dash of bitters for flavouring.

* Fruit juice is an essential alternative to alcohol – orange and apple are both popular.

* Tonic, lemonade, alcohol-free beer and cola are acceptable soft drinks.

CLASSIC COCKTAILS

Bloody Mary

A measure of vodka, topped up with tomato juice, seasoned with a dash of Worcestershire sauce and squeeze of lemon juice. Celery salt and pepper may be added to taste.

Bloody Mary.

Singapore Sling

2 measures gin, 1 measure cherry brandy and 1 measure lemon juice. Serve on ice, topped up with soda water or sparkling mineral water.

Singapore Sling.

Buck's Fizz

Fresh orange juice and champagne in equal proportions.

Dry Martini

A mixture of gin and vermouth, the proportions varying from 3 measures gin to 1 measure vermouth to half and half or 1 measure gin to 2 measures vermouth. Olives are optional.

Gin and It

1 measure gin to 1 measure sweet vermouth.

Harvey Wallbanger

1 measure vodka shaken with 2 measures fresh orange juice, served with a little Galliano liqueur floating on the surface.

Harvey Wallbanger.

COCKTAILS CALENDAR

Make a note of the cocktails you sample or mix, with the date and comments. Seasonal favourites might include warming brandy or whisky cocktails for winter, champagne cocktails for summer and fruity concoctions for autumn.

DATE/OCCASION	COCKTAIL	INGREDIENTS	COMMENTS

A cooling kiwi cocktail for summer.

LIGHT REFRESHMENTS

Provide a selection of bought snacks with drinks – pretzels, tortilla chips, salted nuts and breadsticks are ideal. When you intend serving only snacks, provide tempting canapés and/or a selection of dips.

SPEEDY CANAPES
These sophisticated bites look impressive and taste wonderful but are not difficult to make.

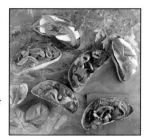

A selection of canapés.

* Use a day-old large loaf of bread, cut it lengthways into medium-thick slices (thin ones will sag easily when topped) and spread with butter. Gently fry chopped onions with thyme and olives. Spread a little *tapenade* on the bread and top with the onion mixture. For a pepper and anchovy topping, place strips of pepper and anchovy in a small bowl and drizzle with olive oil and vinegar. Arrange the peppers and anchovies on the bread and sprinkle with herbs and capers. For a mozzarella and tomato topping, brush the bread with pesto sauce and spoon tomato sauce over each. Arrange a slice of mozzarella cheese on each slice and cover with the tomato strips. Garnish with fresh basil leaves.

Smoked salmon canapés.

* Flavour unsalted butter with grated lemon rind and finely snipped chives and spread on the bread. Trim off the crusts. Top with smoked salmon, cut into small squares and place on serving platters. Whip some double cream with a little lemon juice, then place in a piping bag fitted with a small plain piping nozzle. Pipe a small circle of cream on top of each canapé and finish with a small sprig of dill.

* Spread the bread with fine, smooth pâté, trim off the crusts and cut into fingers. Top with cocktail gherkins, halved lengthways, tiny rolls of thinly sliced smoked chicken or halved radishes.

DIPS
Serve breadsticks, tortilla chips or small crackers with these dips.

Dips are easy to make and always popular.

* Finely chop 225g/8oz onion and cook in a large knob of butter with 15ml/ 1 tbsp fennel seeds until thoroughly softened but not browned, stirring occasionally. Leave to cool. Finely chop a good handful of parsley and 1 garlic clove; stir these into the onion with 225g/8oz/1 cup cream cheese. Season to taste, then chill.

* Peel, seed and chop 4 ripe plum tomatoes. Season well and stir in 2.5ml/½ tsp caster sugar. Gradually mix the tomatoes into 225g/8oz/1 cup ricotta cheese with about 30ml/2 tbsp snipped chives. Finely shred 4–6 basil sprigs and stir them into the dip just before serving.

* Finely chop 1 celery stick, 1 small carrot, a small wedge of white cabbage and 1 spring onion – a food processor is ideal for this. Mix with 225g/8oz/1 cup soft cheese and 115g/4oz/½ cup finely grated Cheddar cheese. Season with salt, pepper and wholegrain mustard to taste.

PARTY FOOD RECORD

Keep a record of the food you serve at parties. Looking back at the canapé ideas you had is great fun and ensures you serve different menus at next year's round of parties.

OCCASION	FOOD SERVED	DATE

✱ PARTY TIP: Try to choose canapés that can be made in advance or kept cool in the refrigerator. There is nothing worse than the host or hostess being stuck in the kitchen and missing out on the party.

BUFFET AND PARTY GUIDE

A buffet can be planned to serve ten to fifty guests in a living-space where no more than six could be comfortably accommodated for a sit-down meal. Serve-yourself menus can be simple, a jolly jumble of tempting dishes or gourmet style in terms of the selection and presentation of food. Remember that all food should be easy to eat with a fork unless you have space for everyone to find a seat and comfortably use a knife and fork.

Simple Buffet Suppers

Dishes do not have to make up a conventional menu as a buffet can be quite varied. Offer dishes which are compatible so that guests are sure to enjoy their meal even if they do not mix the foods in precisely the way you had intended. Include anything from breads, a cheeseboard and salad, to quiches, cold meat platters or an easy-to-serve hot dish, such as a casserole, risotto or hotpot.

Pizzas make good buffet fare. Vary the toppings so there is something for everyone.

Informal Buffet Meal

Plan the menu around one or two main dishes, hot or cold. Casseroles or sauced dishes are suitable; savoury pancakes, layered pasta dishes, rice and couscous main courses all work well. Set out salads or cold dishes in advance, with heatproof mats ready for hot dishes. Later, clear away the main course and set out desserts; these may be arranged to one side of the buffet or on a separate table in advance.

Formal Buffet

Ready-portioned first courses are best: for example, salads, savoury cocktails and mousses can be prepared in glasses or small dishes. Dressed salmon, a baked or boiled ham on the bone, boned and stuffed chicken or a large

Cooked meats and cheeses can look quite spectacular as a cold platter.

terrine of poultry or meat are classic dishes. Hot or cold fish, poultry or meat dishes should be dressed with a sauce or salad dressing and attractively garnished. New potatoes, rice or pasta accompaniments may be served hot or as salads. Vegetable dishes and side salads can be quite complex as long as all ingredients are cut into bite-size portions. A vegetable and bean gratin is often a good choice for a side dish or vegetarian option. Cheese and dessert may be laid out simultaneously, coffee and confectionery should follow.

SERVING TIPS FOR BUFFETS

✳ Congestion at the buffet table always dampens party spirits. Forward planning and gentle encouragement as guests help themselves usually ensures that everyone is served easily and quickly.

✳ When catering for a large number, move the buffet table into the middle of the room, if possible, so that guests can serve themselves from both sides.

✳ Food can be arranged on two or more separate tables. This works well with a formal menu if you put plates and the main dish on one table and serve accompaniments separately.

Cutlery for a casual affair.

The perfect chance to use the family china.

✳ Set out plenty of serving cutlery, with saucers on which to place them, if necessary, when used – as, for example, when setting for a soup, casserole or similarly juicy dish.

✳ Set out plates, cutlery and napkins. When catering for more than ten, stack the plates in two piles at opposite ends of the table. Wrapping cutlery in napkins makes it look neat, but unravelling it can be extremely difficult when standing, holding a plate and trying to make polite conversation.

The neutral colour of this china will not detract from the colourful party food.

✳ Keep drinks completely separate from a food buffet. Provide plenty of other surfaces on which guests can deposit glasses.

✳ For larger gatherings and to save table space, instead of putting out large dishes of food all at once, top them up as they are emptied or replace them with fresh platters.

✳ Cut foods which may be difficult to serve – pastries, terrines and joints or boned poultry. Whole hams look terrific but it is a good idea to carve several portions off the joint so that guests can serve themselves easily. Carve as necessary or encourage more confident guests to carve and others will soon follow suit.

✳ Combine small amounts of similar foods on one large plate rather than leaving untidy, virtually empty dishes on the buffet. Clear away used crockery promptly.

PARTY GUEST RECORD

Keeping a party guest list is an excellent idea – it always serves so many other purposes, like acting as a reminder when last year's Christmas card list is lost! For super-efficient records, use different coloured pens or a highlighter to differentiate between different levels of acquaintances. For example, you may like to write the names of close friends in red, so that you know always to include that number for parties, and to list colleagues or relatives in blue and green. Use your colour coding to check on the likely number of guests you would want to invite to different types of parties. It is a good idea to add any special notes alongside names. For example, you may want to include a reminder if particular couples did not enjoy each other's company on a previous occasion or if certain acquaintances have babysitter problems, so prefer lunchtime invitations.

NAME	NOTES	NAME	NOTES

REFRESHMENT REMINDER RECORD

Make a note of the date, occasion and type of food served for buffets and drinks parties. Remember to jot down details of any particularly successful combinations.

DATE

OCCASION

REFRESHMENTS

NOTES

DATE

OCCASION

REFRESHMENTS

NOTES

DATE

OCCASION

REFRESHMENTS

NOTES

DATE

OCCASION

REFRESHMENTS

NOTES

✳ REFRESHMENT TIP: A spectacular light buffet can be conjured up from a well-planned shopping session. Platters of salamis, cold meats and other charcuterie products can be set out with a cheese-board or two, pickles and bottled Italian marinated vegetables. A huge basket filled with a splendid array of international breads and bowls of cherry tomatoes will complete the simplest buffet meal.

CHEESEBOARD TIPS

Choose cheese with care.

✳ Cheese is popular with most people and makes an excellent addition to any menu. Nowadays most good supermarkets stock an impressive range, but it is always worth finding a specialist shop for special treats.

✳ It is better to offer two or three excellent cheeses than to buy a wide variety of inferior pieces.

✳ Select different types of cheese – a piece each of hard, semi-soft and blue cheese makes a good board.

✳ Buy cheese that is ripe for serving, particularly when selecting a semi-soft cheese, such as Brie, which should be smooth and creamy right through, without a layer of firm chalky flesh in the middle.

✳ Bring the cheese to room temperature well before it is served.

✳ Provide different knives for cutting firm and soft cheeses, and one knife exclusively for blue cheese.

✳ Serve plain biscuits with the cheese course – water biscuits, Bath Olivers and oatcakes are all suitable. Thin, crisp Melba toast is also a good choice. Flavoured biscuits and crackers ruin a good cheese served at the end of a meal.

✳ Grapes, pears and apples all go well with cheese. Fresh dates and figs are especially good with goat's cheese and semi-soft cheeses. Celery is also an ideal accompaniment.

Grapes go well with cheese.

✳ Fresh nuts in the shell may be served – walnuts, pecans and brazils are the best choice. Remember to put out the nutcrackers.

✳ A full-bodied red wine or port may be served with the cheese course. Many people prefer cheese after the main course, before the dessert, while others like to round off the meal on a savoury note. Unless you have particularly strong feelings on the subject, the usual solution is to bring both cheese and dessert to the table at once and allow guests to choose.

An invitation to indulge.

FAVOURITE CHEESE RECORD

It can be infuriating to sample a delicious new cheese for a dinner party, then forget its name and find that the store does not have it on display next time you look for it. Keep a list of cheeses sampled, the date and place of purchase, and your personal tasting notes.

CHEESE	DATE	PURCHASED FROM	TASTING NOTES

BARBECUE REMINDERS

Barbecue parties can be entirely informal family affairs or equally relaxed culinary extravaganzas. The choice of food depends on the occasion – burgers, sausages, chops, ribs and steaks are great for all the family; seafood, large joints or whole poultry and foods *en brochette* are ideal for more sophisticated gatherings. Whatever the food, there are a few golden rules of planning to remember.

TECHNICAL/SAFETY CHECKS
* Make sure you have sufficient grilling space for the number of people you plan to invite or the type of food being cooked.
* Stock up on charcoal or other fuel, remembering that old fuel left over from a previous season may be damp and difficult to burn successfully.
* Ensure that you have lighting fuel, firelighters or suitable kindling.
* Check that you have sufficient gas for a gas-fuelled barbecue; if in doubt buy an additional cylinder.
* Light the barbecue at least 30 minutes before you want to begin cooking. Depending on the size of barbecue, the fuel can take up to 45 minutes to burn through until it is hot enough to cook food.

Instant charcoal

Charcoal briquettes

Lumpwood charcoal

Coconut-shell charcoal

Woodchips and herbs

Wood

* The barbecue is ready for cooking when flames and smoke have subsided and the coals look grey and slightly ashen, but give off a vast amount of heat.
* When there are children and pets milling around, be sure that an adult is always close to take charge of the barbecue. Warn children to stand well clear and never leave young children unattended to play near the barbecue.
* If the barbecue party becomes particularly jolly, make sure that the chef stays safely sober until the cooking is over.

Never pour petrol, paraffin or other fuel directly on to the barbecue, not even when it appears to have stopped burning or not to have lit properly. Use proper barbecue lighting fuel and follow the manufacturer's instructions closely.

FOOD FORETHOUGHTS
* Plan to serve light nibbles while the food is cooking. Dips and crudités are ideal.
* Think about the numbers and the batches in which food can be cooked when planning the menu. Include small items which cook quickly as well as some that take longer, so that guests have something to eat fairly promptly.
* Kettle barbecues and other types of covered barbecue are ideal for cooking large joints and whole poultry – even large turkeys – but do calculate the cooking time and put the food on to cook in good time. Allow a little extra time to rest the food. If you are new to barbecueing, avoid large items as if you have problems with the fire they can prove difficult.

A barbecue is a wonderful way of entertaining friends and family.

✳ Make use of the conventional oven when cooking for a crowd; for example, chicken portions can be virtually cooked in the oven, then finished on the barbecue. The same applies to sausages, which can be three-quarters cooked but not browned, then crisped on the barbecue.

A kettle barbecue.

✳ Never mix raw and cooked foods on the same plate or surface area. Establish an efficient cooking rota so that raw foods do not touch those that are nearly cooked, and have clean platters and separate utensils for handling food which is about to be served.

✳ Potatoes can be baked conventionally, new potatoes boiled and substantial salads served to complement the grilled specialities.

Turn hamburgers carefully.

BEST BARBECUES RECORDS

Keep a record of successful barbecues for future reference. Remember to include notes of anything particularly interesting, such as using an unusual type of fuel or sprinkling a smoking agent or herbs on the burning coals. As ever, a guest list and note of the dishes will ensure you do not repeat the same performance too often and provide inspiration for future occasions.

BARBECUE OCCASION	BARBECUE OCCASION
DATE	DATE
GUEST LIST	GUEST LIST
MENU	MENU
CHEF'S NOTES	CHEF'S NOTES

✳ BARBECUE TIP: Remember to check whether all the guests eat fish, poultry and meat, then make suitable arrangements if you have invited vegetarians. Cooking vegetables alongside animal foods is likely to be unacceptable as the meat juices will spit and flavour the vegetarian food. A small hibachi grill or disposable barbecue can be used instead, but try to be discreet and do not make the vegetarian alternative look like a poor offering, cooked in a corner. Another solution is to barbecue the vegetarian food first, wrap it in foil and keep it hot on one side of the grill.

BARBECUE OCCASION	BARBECUE OCCASION
DATE	DATE
GUEST LIST	GUEST LIST
MENU	MENU
CHEF'S NOTES	CHEF'S NOTES

PICNIC PLANNER

The accent is on colour and freshness.

Nothing matches the freedom of eating alfresco meals on a warm summer's day out in the country air.

Whether you are planning on dining from a Victorian-style hamper in an elegant lakeside setting or packing a modest packed lunch for a day's hike in the country, here are a few thoughts to consider.

✳ Always wrap food well to prevent damage and keep it fresh. Plastic bags, clear film and foil are all useful. Rigid containers provide protection for delicate items, and water-tight containers are essential for liquids, such as salad dressings or sauces.

✳ Baked items, such as quiche, meat loaf, pies or cake,

Hampers make handy containers.

are best packed in the container in which they were cooked. If suitable, wash and dry the container, then line it with clear film or foil and replace the food before wrapping the whole lot in a plastic bag.

✳ Use an insulated box or bag to keep foods that are normally refrigerated cool. Small insulated containers are available for individual packed lunches. Freezer-chilled sleeves are ideal for chilling bottles of drink which should additionally be placed in an insulated bag or box.

✳ Disposable plates and plastic cutlery are useful for fun outings; reasonable-quality plastic ware will last for years and it does not bend or flop as you are trying to eat; proper china and glassware is essential for grand picnics, and packing it well with layers of clean dish

Earth-toned linen looks lovely at an alfresco celebration.

towels or kitchen paper will avoid damage.

✳ Pack a waterproof ground sheet or plastic dust sheet, a rug to lay over the top and a cloth on which to set out the food. Napkins, kitchen towel, dish towels, damp face wipes and a large bag for rubbish are other non-food items to remember. Do not forget the bottle-opener.

Unbreakable glasses can be very handsome.

 # MEMORABLE PICNICS RECORD

Make a note of successful picnics for future reference – you may think you will always remember precisely where you went and what you took, but it is easy to forget important details.

PICNIC DATE	PICNIC DATE
THE LOCATION	THE LOCATION
HAMPER RECORD	HAMPER RECORD
THE PICNIC PEOPLE	THE PICNIC PEOPLE
NOTES – ACTIVITIES/OCCASION	NOTES – ACTIVITIES/OCCASION

✳ PICNIC TIP: For a thoroughly stylish and practical picnic hamper, try one of the latest wicker-sytle baskets or carriers that come with an insulated lining to keep food and drink cool. With care, one should last for years.

HAMPER TALK

Sandwiches, pasties, fresh fruit and cookies are typical away-day food, but there are all sorts of exciting dishes to elevate the picnic to gourmet standards.

TO BEGIN ...

Potted foods are ideal for picnics.

＊ A bowl of cream cheese sharpened with lemon juice, softened with a little fromage frais, then flavoured with some black olive paste and snipped chives makes a delicious dip for peeled cooked tiger prawns (leave the tails on), chunks of good-quality garlic sausage and cherry tomatoes. Pack cocktail sticks for dipping the garlic sausage.

＊ Wrap large peeled prawns (with tails) in butter-brushed filo, leaving the tails exposed; short fingers of smoked ham can be enclosed in filo pastry; or halved canned artichoke bottoms rolled in freshly grated Parmesan can be wrapped in the pastry. Bake until golden brown, then cool on a wire rack before packing. Serve with a perky olive oil and cider vinegar dressing, laced with fresh garlic and a hint of chilli sauce, for dipping the pastries.

Filo pastries are tasty and easy to eat, perfect with prawns or a chilli dipping sauce.

TO SAVOUR ...

Galantine of chicken.

＊ Galantine of chicken – a boned, stuffed bird – makes a spectacular picnic centre-piece. Order the boned bird from the butcher, pack with a firm stuffing and cool completely after cooking before wrapping and chilling. A dressing of blue cheese and fromage frais or yogurt may be served as a sauce.

＊ Meat loaf takes on a new image when made with minced chicken or turkey, with a layer of sage and onion stuffing enriched with a little chopped bacon and chicken livers. Mix the normal basic ingredients (onion, breadcrumbs, egg) with minced poultry. Place half in the tin and top with a savoury stuffing, then add the rest of the poultry. Serve with a sauce of mayonnaise and soured cream.

LINGER OVER ...

Fruit pastry tartlets.

＊ Little fruit pastry tartlets, filled with a shallow layer of colourful fruit and served with whipped cream.

＊ A lemon Swiss roll (simply add the grated rind of 1 lemon when whisking the eggs and sugar) filled with lemon curd, served sliced with a slightly sweetened strawberry purée and thin pouring cream.

FAVOURITE PICNIC FOOD RECORD

RECIPE TITLE	RECIPE TITLE
DATE	DATE
SERVES	SERVES
INGREDIENTS	INGREDIENTS

METHOD

METHOD

✱ PICNIC TIP: Sparkling wine is wonderful for summer picnics, but always remember the drivers in the party. Take plenty of sparkling mineral water and lots of fresh citrus fruit with a small pot of honey to add interest to alcohol-free drinks. A cool box is very useful for keeping drinks nicely chilled. It can also be used to stop sandwiches becoming hot and limp.

FOOD FOR FESTIVALS

From simple family repasts to state banquets, sharing a meal is an important part of celebrating in every culture throughout the world.

Chanukah

This December Jewish festival of light is a time when traditional dishes are served, particularly the universally popular *latkes*, or grated potato pancakes.

Christmas

There are many international culinary specialities: roast turkey, goose or sucking pig are traditional. On Christmas Eve in Poland, a stuffed carp graces the table and a sweet poppy seed dessert is served. One famous French dish is *Bûche de Noël*, a rich chocolate Swiss roll, and roast goose or turkey is served on Christmas Eve for the main festive meal. From Italy comes tall *panettone*, a delicious yeasted cake flavoured with vanilla, or rich *panforte*, a dense sweetmeat of spiced dried fruit and nuts.

The Christmas turkey is a festive treat.

Easter

Hot cross buns, simnel cake (a fruit cake enclosing a layer of almond paste) and decorated chocolate eggs are typical Easter fare. Rich yeasted breads and cakes are baked in Eastern European countries; lamb is internationally traditional for the main celebration meal. In Italy *cassata alla Siciliana* is prepared: a light sponge layered with a rich filling of mascarpone cheese and crystallized or candied fruits, covered with chocolate icing.

Hot cross buns.

The harvest loaf is a potent symbol.

Harvest Festival

An elaborate loaf in the shape of a sheaf of corn, glazed and baked until golden brown, is often displayed with freshly harvested fruit and vegetables for this festival of thanksgiving.

Thanksgiving

An American and Canadian feast celebrated in November and October respectively. Roast turkey and pumpkin pie are among the celebratory dishes.

New Year

Every culture celebrates its new year with foods that reflect hope for the future. Rosh Hashanah, the Jewish New Year, celebrated in September/October, is an occasion for eating sweet foods, such as apples with honey. Cholla, the plaited bread, is shaped in a circle in the hope of fullness and completeness. The Chinese New Year is a time for great feasting, with multi-course meals being served. The Japanese New Year celebrations stretch over a period of days, during which time dishes reflecting hopes for prosperity, health and good harvest are prepared.

Cholla bread is traditionally baked to celebrate Rosh Hashanah.

Ramadan

A period of fasting for Muslims, when food is not eaten from dawn to sunset. A dried fruit salad with apricots, prunes and nuts scented with rose water or orange flower water is traditional during breaks in the fast, eaten in the middle of the meal, with rice, wheat and the meat dish.

Shrove Tuesday pancakes can be simple or sophisticated.

Pancake Day or Shrove Tuesday

Before the Lenten period of fasting, the house was traditionally cleared of rich foods, like eggs. Being the ideal recipe for using up eggs and creamy milk, pancakes are traditionally served on the eve of Ash Wednesday, the first day of Lent.

Passover or Pesach

During the eight-day Jewish festival of Passover, wheat flour is forbidden and matzos are eaten instead of bread. The formal meal on the eve of the feast includes chopped liver, roast chicken and a special sponge cake. Ingredients of particular significance to the feast are displayed ceremoniously and the meal is concluded by eating a piece of matzo.

Matzo pancakes.

FAMILY FESTIVAL RECORD

Keep a record of feast days and the way in which they are celebrated in your home. Revive all the traditions from your childhood, jot them down and pass them on to future generations to ensure they are not forgotten.

FEAST	FEAST
DATE	DATE
CELEBRATIONS	CELEBRATIONS
FESTIVE FOODS	FESTIVE FOODS
FEAST	FEAST
DATE	DATE
CELEBRATIONS	CELEBRATIONS
FESTIVE FOODS	FESTIVE FOODS

✳ FESTIVAL TIP: Encourage your parents – or grandparents – to tell you all about their traditional family celebrations. Search through books for specific recipes, make all the preparations and plan a nostalgic party. This sort of party would be a wonderful and evocative way of celebrating an older person's birthday or wedding anniversary.

EASTER SIMNEL CAKE

Half-way through Lent, it is the custom to make a simnel cake which is brought out to celebrate Easter Day and the end of the Lenten fast. It is as much a part of the Easter festival as hot cross buns and painted eggs.
Makes a 25cm/10inch cake

INGREDIENTS
115g/4oz/1 cup plain flour
225g/8oz/2 cups self-raising flour
5ml/1 tsp ground mixed spice
225g/8oz/1½ cups raisins
225g/8oz/1½ cups currants
225g/8oz/1½ cups sultanas
50g/2oz/⅓ cup chopped candied peel
115g/4oz/½ cup glacé cherries, washed,
  dried and halved
115g/4oz/1 cup ground almonds
225g/8oz/1 cup butter
225g/8oz/1 cup light soft brown sugar
4 eggs
juice of 1 orange
30ml/2 tbsp apricot jam, warmed and sieved
675g/1½ lb marzipan or almond paste

Preheat the oven to 160°C/325°F/Gas 3. Line and grease a 25cm/10inch round deep cake tin. Sift both types of flour with the mixed spice. Mix the raisins, currants, sultanas, peel and cherries in a bowl. Sprinkle two spoonfuls of the flour mixture over the fruit and add the ground almonds, then mix well.

An Easter simnel cake.

Cream together the butter and sugar until very soft and pale. Carefully beat in the eggs, one at a time, adding a little of the flour mixture after each addition to prevent the mixture from curdling. Fold in the remaining flour mixture using a large metal spoon. Then fold in the fruit mixture and the orange juice. Turn the mixture into the tin and spread it evenly with a palette knife. Bake the cake for 3½-3¾ hours. Cover the top loosely with a piece of foil after the first 2 hours to prevent it from browning.

Insert a metal skewer into the middle of the cake to check if it is cooked. It should come out without any sticky mixture clinging to it. If there is mixture on the skewer, continue baking the cake, checking after a further 15 minutes. Remove the cake from the tin and cool on a wire rack.

Brush the top of the cake with a thin layer of apricot jam. Roll out a third of the marzipan or almond paste to cover the top, and place on top of the jam. Use the remaining marzipan to make a plait or rope for the border of the cake and 11 balls to decorate the top. You could even try shaping marzipan chicks.

RICH PUMPKIN PIE

This classic American pie is an important part of the Thanksgiving celebrations. For a real treat, add a dash of brandy and a little icing sugar to double cream and whip it until soft and light, then serve it generously swirled on each rich slice.

Serves 8–10

INGREDIENTS

175g/6oz/³⁄4 cup unsalted butter
225g/8oz/2 cups plain flour
50g/2oz/¹⁄4 cup caster sugar
30–45ml/2–3 tbsp water

Filling
450g/1lb pumpkin, peeled and seeded
3 eggs
5ml/1 tsp natural vanilla essence
5ml/1 tsp ground cinnamon
5ml/1 tsp ground ginger
2.5ml/¹⁄2 tsp grated nutmeg
2.5ml/¹⁄2 tsp ground mace
pinch of ground cloves
grated rind of 1 orange
115g/4oz/³⁄4 cup soft light brown sugar
250ml/8fl oz/1 cup double cream
45ml/3 tbsp brandy

Rub the butter into the flour until the mixture resembles fine breadcrumbs, then stir in the sugar. Mix in just enough water to bind the ingredients into clumps, then press them together. Roll out this pastry and use to line a deep 25cm/10in flan tin or dish. Prick the pastry base all over with a fork or skewer and chill for 15 minutes.

Pumpkin pie is part of the Thanksgiving feast.

Set the oven at 200°C/400°F/Gas 6. Line the pastry case with greaseproof paper, add baking beans, then bake for around 20 minutes. Take out of the oven, remove the paper and reduce the oven temperature to 180°C/350°F/Gas 4.

Chop up the pumpkin into small cubes. Steam the cubed pumpkin for 10–15 minutes until soft, and leave to drain. Place the cooled pumpkin in a food processor with all the remaining ingredients and blend to a smooth texture. Pour into the prepared pastry case and bake for 1¼ hours until the filling is set and lightly browned. Leave to cool slightly. Pumpkin pie can be served hot or cold, but it is best when eaten warm with whipped cream.

Festive Recipe Record

Keep a record of your favourite festive recipes here.

Recipe Title	Recipe Title
Origins	Origins
Date	Date
Serves	Serves
Ingredients	Ingredients
Method	Method

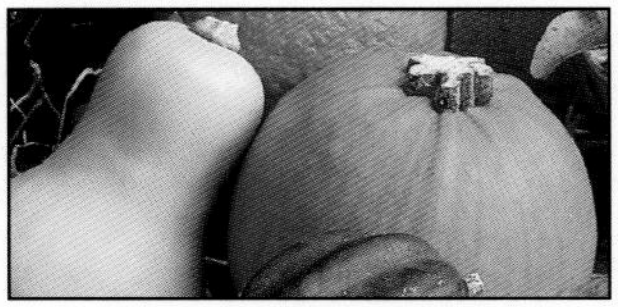

✷ FESTIVE TIP: Notes that are practical for today's busy cook are just as important as details of the origins of festive foods. If you discover a dish that was fantastic when frozen, thawed and reheated, then do make a note of this alongside your recipe. Even though you think you will always remember, you may well have forgotten the details by next year.

COOK AHEAD FOR CHRISTMAS

Many traditional Christmas foods should be prepared months in advance so that they have time to mature. These are some of the items to set aside in the store-cupboard and some that can be frozen a few days or weeks before the festive holiday.

Apple Sauce
This can be made and frozen months ahead: it is a good idea to make a supply when you have a glut of home-harvested fruit.

Brandy Butter or Hard Sauce
Made with equal quantities of sugar to butter and well flavoured with brandy, this will keep for 2 weeks in a covered dish in the fridge. It can be frozen for up to 4 months, so make it well in advance.

Cut out shapes from brandy butter and serve on Christmas pudding.

Bread Sauce
A traditional accompaniment for roast turkey, this can be made and frozen a couple of weeks in advance and can save you precious time on the day.

Chestnuts
Cook and peel chestnuts, then freeze them ready for making stuffing. They are also delicious sautéed with onions and bacon, and mixed with Brussels sprouts.

Christmas cake – the cook's turn to shine.

Christmas Cake
A rich fruit cake should mature for at least 6 weeks. Allow another week for the marzipan coating to set before covering the cake with icing and at least 1–2 days for the icing to set.

Christmas Pudding or Plum Pudding

The best puddings are prepared at least 2 months before Christmas so that they have time to mature. Do not despair if you are running late – a home-made pudding that is not as rich as it might be will taste better than most bought alternatives. Remember to remove the covering from the pudding as soon as it is cooked. When cold, place it in a clean basin and 'feed' it with a little brandy or rum, then wrap it in clear film or double greaseproof paper and place in a tightly closed plastic bag.

Christmas pudding.

Cranberry Sauce

This can be made and kept chilled in a covered container for 1–2 weeks, depending on the quantity of sugar. It also freezes well. Recipes with a high proportion of sugar will keep for months.

Mincemeat

This rich preserve should be well laced with brandy or rum and allowed to mature for 3 months. A traditional recipe needs at least 4 weeks for the flavours to mingle, otherwise it tastes weak. A lighter recipe, with more apple and lemon, can be prepared and used fresh or after a few days, but it is not the same as the full-flavoured preserve.

Pickles and Chutneys

Do remember to stock up with pickled onions, pickled red cabbage and chutney. From September onwards, start stocking up the storecupboard with traditional relishes for cold turkey and ham. Last-minute pickles include peaches in a sweet-sour vinegar and pickled eggs, which should be matured for 2 weeks and eaten within 6 weeks for best texture.

Chutneys and pickles are essential for serving with cold turkey and ham.

Stuffings

These can be made a week or so ahead and frozen. Freeze breadcrumb-based stuffings dry, then add milk or the required binding agent when the mixture has been thawed.

CHRISTMAS COOK-AHEAD CHART

Use your chart as a reminder as well as a record. Tick off the foods as they are prepared, entering the names of chutneys and preserves, and listing any other dishes you cook and freeze. Use the chart as a guide for drawing up an annual record.

YEAR

FOOD	MADE	READY	NOTES
Christmas Cake			
Christmas Pudding			
Chutneys			
Mincemeat			
Pickles			
Dishes in Freezer			

✳ CHRISTMAS TIP: A rich Christmas pudding or mincemeat, well laced with brandy, will keep for a whole year or even longer. So make a large batch one year and you will be ready for the next season too! Puddings also make great presents, particularly for someone not so keen on cooking. However, remember to use vegetable suet if giving one to a vegetarian.

YEAR

FOOD	MADE	READY	NOTES
Christmas Cake			
Christmas Pudding			
Chutneys			
Mincemeat			
Pickles			
Dishes in Freezer			

YEAR

FOOD	MADE	READY	NOTES
Christmas Cake			
Christmas Pudding			
Chutneys			
Mincemeat			
Pickles			
Dishes in Freezer			

✷ CHRISTMAS TIP: Stock up the freezer with a few simple dishes to lighten the load of rich foods over Christmas menus. A simple quiche, fish pie, seafood lasagne or some home-made fish cakes are excellent for light suppers or snack lunches. Children in particular get rather overwhelmed by lots of rich food, so stock up with some of their favourite snacks.

 **CHRISTMAS DINNER RECORD**

Keep a record of guests who come for Christmas dinner and the food you serve.

GUESTS	FOOD SERVED	YEAR

GOURMET GIFTS

Of all the home-made items that can be given, food gifts are by far the most gratifying as they are unlikely to be unacceptable on grounds of personal preference. Here are a few ideas for slightly unusual gourmet gifts.

Peach Wine

This is not really a proper wine at all, but a delicious and refreshing amalgam of peaches, wine and *eau de vie*. Drink in the summer, either on its own or diluted with soda water. Peel and halve 6 ripe peaches, then poach them in 1 litre/1¾ pints/4 cups dry white wine for 15 minutes, until tender. Cover and allow to stand overnight.

Peach wine.

Remove the peaches, then strain the liquid through a coffee filter. Add 200g/7oz/scant cup caster sugar and 175ml/6fl oz/¾ cup *eau de vie* and stir to dissolve the sugar. Pour into clean, dry, sterilized bottles and cork. Store in the fridge. Drink within two weeks. Serve well chilled.

Flavoured Vinegars

Cider vinegar or white wine vinegar can be flavoured as for oils. Fruit vinegars are excellent for salad dressings or flavouring sauces. Raspberries, blackcurrants

Flavoured vinegars.

and plums are ideal – simply leave the fruit in the vinegar for a few days, crushing it occasionally, then strain it through a fine sieve. Strain the vinegar through a paper coffee filter and sweeten it, if liked, with sugar.

Flavoured Oils

Herbs (such as bay leaves, thyme, tarragon and basil), garlic, cinnamon sticks, juniper berries, fennel seeds and other flavouring ingredients can be infused in oil ready for cooking or for use in dressings. A light oil, such as sunflower, can be used or olive oil can be flavoured.

Flavoured oils.

Pickled Onions

Heat the spiced vinegar with sugar to taste and 2 bay leaves for each jar of onions. Pack the bay leaves with the onions.

Pots of pickles.

Shortbread

A perennial favourite, a good buttery shortbread is always appreciated, even by those who are not so keen on sweet things. Use these proportions for sure success – they always give melt-in-the-mouth results.

Buttery shortbread.

Cream 175g/6oz/¾ cup butter with 75g/3oz/¾ cup icing sugar until very pale and soft and creamy, then mix in 250g/9oz/2¼ cups plain flour. Press into two greased 15cm/6in tins, prick all over and mark the edge with a fork. Bake at 160°C/325°F/Gas 3 for 50–60 minutes. Stand in the tins for 15 minutes, then cool on a rack.

PRESENTATION IDEAS

Finishing touches can turn an everyday item into something special. A simple pot of jam, for instance, becomes a special gift when it is presented in a pretty jar with the lid covered by a beautiful autumn leaf tied on with raffia. And a bottle of aromatic chilli oil does not need a written label to identify the flavourings when its neck is decorated with a bunch of chillies.

LEFT:
A decorative touch turns this lemon- and lime-flavoured vinegar into a perfect gift.

BELOW:
Natural materials make inexpensive packaging.

ABOVE:
The autumnal colours of the pot-pourri are echoed in the matt-brown ribbon and the sisal string used to decorate the cellophane bag.

RIGHT:
A dried orange slice tied around a jar of marmalade is an unusual but eloquent label.

FOOD GIFT RECORD AND IDEAS

Make use of these pages not only to keep a record of the food presents you make, but of the many good ideas that spring to mind in the course of cooking that are always forgotten when someone's birthday comes around. Any occasion is an opportunity for a food gift – birthdays, anniversaries, Easter, Christmas, visiting friends for a weekend, or as a get-well token or congratulations present.

FOOD GIFT	GIVEN TO	DATE	OCCASION

INDEX